the Fun-to-Sing Songbook

To the memory of the two Morton Nelsons . . .
father and son, who I go on loving.

the Fun-to-Sing Songbook

BY

ESTHER L. NELSON

ILLUSTRATIONS BY JOYCE BEHR

Sterling Publishing Co., Inc. New York

By the Same Author

Dancing Games for Children of All Ages
The Funny Songbook
The Great Rounds Songbook
Holiday Singing and Dancing Games
Movement Games for Children of All Ages
Musical Games for Children of All Ages
The Silly Songbook
Singing and Dancing Games for the Very Young

Thanks to friends known and unknown who have helped with this collection: Risa Sokolsky, Janet Robinson, Ruth Melnick Robinson, Susan Greenblatt, Phyllis Grilikhes Maxwell, Trudy Hill, Shulamis Levin Friedman, Fay Storch, Jane Notter, Robert Benson, and Ruth Jacobson for sharing her extensive library with me. And a public declaration of thanks and love to my editor and dear friend Sheila Barry for guiding me successfully to the completion of nine books.

Published by Sterling Publishing Co., Inc.
Two Park Avenue, New York, N.Y. 10016
Distributed in Canada by Oak Tree Press Ltd.
% Canadian Manda Group, P.O. Box 920, Station U
Toronto, Ontario, Canada M8Z 5P9
Distributed in the United Kingdom by Blandford Press
Link House, West Street, Poole, Dorset BH15 1LL, England
Distributed in Australia by Capricorn Ltd.
P.O. Box 665, Lane Cove, NSW 2066
Manufactured in the United States of America
All rights reserved

Library of Congress Cataloging-in-Publication Data

The Fun-to-sing songbook.

Children's songs.
Includes index.
Summary: An illustrated collection of fun-to-sing humorous songs, including camp songs, parodies, chants, silly ditties, many classics, and some new songs. Easy-to-play piano accompaniments with guitar chord symbols.
1. Humorous songs. [1. Humorous songs. 2. Songs]
I. Nelson, Esther L. II. Behr, Joyce, ill.
M1992.N   86-752869
ISBN 0-8069-4760-8
ISBN 0-8069-4761-6 (lib. bdg.)
ISBN 0-8069-4762-4 (pbk.)

CONTENTS

QUICK & QUIRKY

I've Got One Head

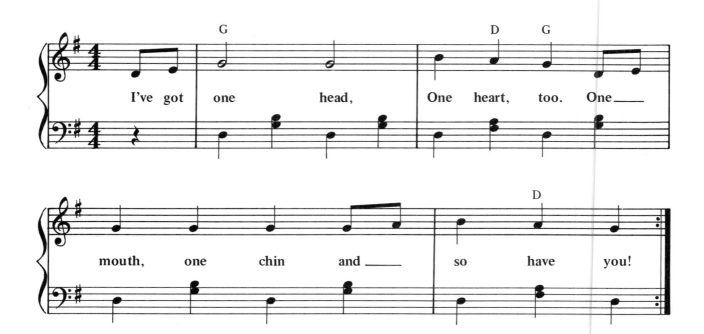

I've got one head,
One heart, too.
One mouth, one chin,
And so have you!

I've got two eyes,
Two ears, too.
Two arms, two legs,
And so have you!

I've got three thoughts,
And three dreams, too.
Three rhymes, three songs,
And so have you!

I've got four limbs,
Two and two.
Four fingers, a thumb,
And so have you!

I've got five toes,
And five more, too.
Five and five makes ten,
And so have you!

I've got no sense,
No dollars, too.
I'm out of my mind,
And so are you!

I Had a Little Dog

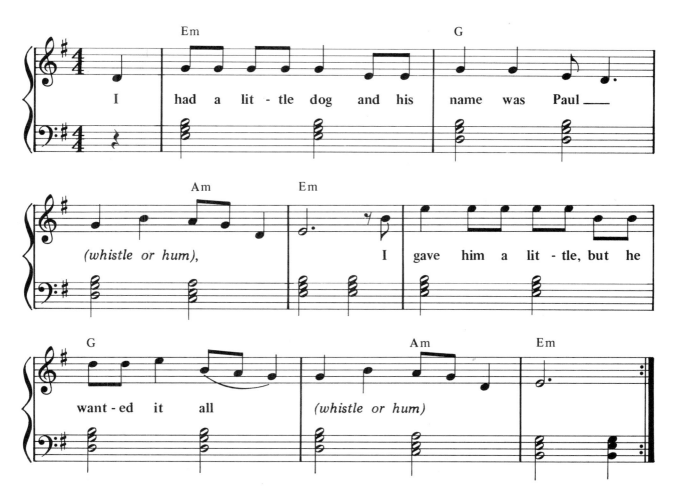

I had a little dog
And his name was Paul *(whistle or hum)*,
I gave him a little,
But he wanted it all *(whistle or hum)*.

I had a little dog
And his name was Maynard *(whistle or hum)*,
I gave him an inch,
But he took the whole yard *(whistle or hum)*.

I had a little dog
And his name was Cheers *(whistle or hum)*,
Both his legs ran to paws
And his head ran to ears *(whistle or hum)*.

I had a little dog
And his name was Rover *(whistle or hum)*,
And when he was shedding,
He shedded all over *(whistle or hum)*.

I had a little dog
And her name was Billie *(whistle or hum)*,
And when she dressed up,
She sure acted silly *(whistle or hum)*.

I had a little dog
And her name was Honey *(whistle or hum)*,
When she gave you her paw,
She looked at you funny *(whistle or hum)*.

I With I Were

If you have trouble deciphering this song, just substitute a "s" or a "sh" in most of the spots where you see a "th."

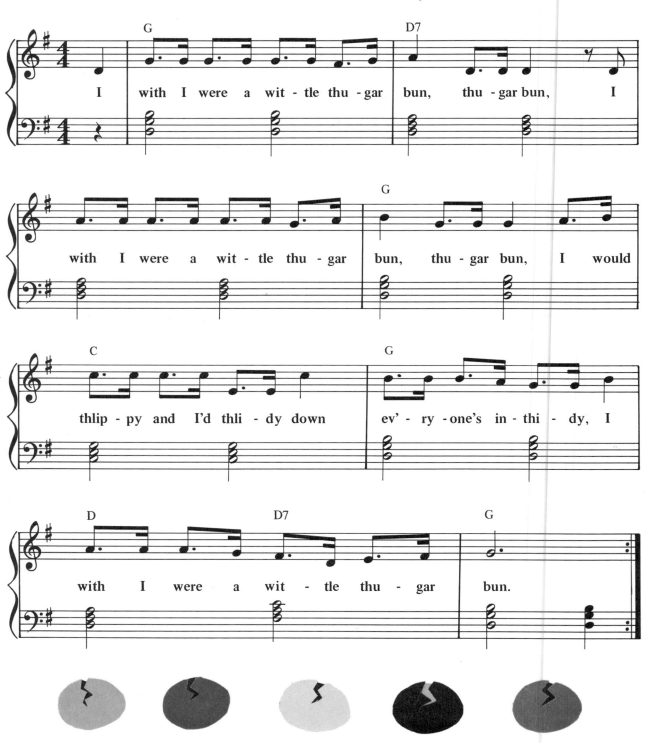

I With I Were

I with I were a wittle thugar bun, thugar
    bun,
I with I were a wittle thugar bun, thugar
    bun,
I would thlippy and I'd thlidy down
    ev'ryone's inthidy,
I with I were a wittle thugar bun.

I with I were a wittle cake of thoap,
    cake of thoap,
I with I were a wittle cake of thoap,
    cake of thoap,
I would thlippy and I'd thlidy on
    ev'rybody's hidie,
I with I were a wittle cake of thoap.

I with I were a fithy in the thea, in the
    thea,
I with I were a fithy in the thea, in the
    thea,
I would thwimy 'round tho cutey, without
    a bathing thuity,
I with I were a fithy in the thea.

I with I were a wittle mothquito,
    mothquito,
I with I were a wittle mothquito,
    mothquito,
I would buthie and I'd bitie through
    ev'rybody's nightie,
I with I were a wittle mothquito.

I with I were a wittle thafety pin, thafety
    pin,
I with I were a wittle thafety pin, thafety
    pin.
I'd get cruthty and I'd ruthty until
    ev'rything went buthty,
I with I were a wittle thafety pin.

I with I were a wittle thippery thlime,
    thippery thlime,
I with I were a wittle thippery thlime,
    thippery thlime,
I would oothey, oothey, oothey in
    ev'rybody's shoe-thieth,
I with I were a wittle thippery thlime.

I with I weren't thuch a thilly thimp,
    thilly thimp,
I with I weren't thuch a thilly thimp,
    thilly thimp,
I'd thing a thuper thong that had thenthe
    and wathn't w'ong,
I with I weren't thuch a thilly thimp.

Three Little Piggies

Three Little Piggies

There was an old sow had three little
    piggies,
Three little piggies had she.
And the old sow always went,
  (spoken) "Grunt, grunt, grunt,"
And the little piggies went,
  (in a high falsetto voice) "Wee, wee,
    wee."

Said one little piggie to the other two
    piggies,
To the other two piggies, said he,
"Why can't we go, "Grunt, grunt,
    grunt,"
Instead of saying "Wee, wee, wee"?

Now these three piggies grew skinny and
    lean,
A very sad sight to see.
Because they kept trying to grunt, grunt,
    grunt,
Instead of going, "Wee, wee, wee."

And these three piggies, they upped and
    died,
Upped and died, all three.
And the moral is never go, "Grunt,
    grunt, grunt,"
If you can only go "Wee, wee, wee."

There Was an Old Woman

You can also sing this song as a round in two parts.

There was an old woman lived under a hill, and if she's not gone, she's living there still.

There was an old woman
Lived under a hill,
And if she's not gone,
She's living there still.

There was an old owl
So lonely and mute.
And if he's silent,
He won't give a hoot.

There was an old frog
On a green lily pad,
He may not be croaking,
But he's feeling bad.

There was an old monkey
Who climbed up a tree,
And when he fell down,
He said, "Excuse me."

There was an old crow
Who sat in the sun,
And when he flew off
Alas, there was none.

There was an old worm
Who ate up a cow,
And then it ate two,
But I don't know how.

14

Over in the Meadow

Over in the Meadow

Over in the meadow in a nest in a tree,
Lived an old Mother birdie, and her little
    birdies three.
"Fly," said the Mother. "We fly," said
    the three,
So they flew and they grew in the nest in
    the tree.

Over in the meadow, in the sand in the
    sun,
Lived an old Daddy froggy and his little
    froggy one.
"Hop," said the Daddy. "We hop," said
    the one.
So they hopped and they plopped in the
    sand in the sun.

Over in the meadow, in a web in a den,
Lived an old Mother spider, and her little
    spiders ten.
"Spin," said the Mother. "We spin," said
    the ten,
So they spun and got done in their web
    in the den.

Over in the meadow, in a house with a
    door,
Lived an old Daddy tom-cat, and his
    little kittens four.
"Creep," said the Daddy. "We creep,"
    said the four,
So they crept and they slept in the house
    with the door.

Over in the meadow, in the deep blue
    sea,
Lived an old Mother fish, and her little
    fishes three.
"Swim," said the Mother. "We swim,"
    said the three,
So they swam and they fam in the deep
    blue sea.

Over in the meadow 'neath a rock that
    was damp,
Lived a group of salamanders who were
    just a little cramped.
"Crawl," said their Daddy, "We crawl,"
    said the flock,
So they crawled and they sprawled 'till
    they found another rock.

A Horse Named Bill

A Horse Named Bill

I had a horse, his name was Bill,
And when he ran, he couldn't stand still.
He ran away one day,
And also I ran with him.

He ran so hard, he couldn't stop,
He ran into a barber shop.
He fell exhausted with his teeth
In the barber's left shoulder.

Oh, I went out into the woods last year,
To hunt for fleas and not for deer,
Because I am—no, I ain't—
The world's best sharpshooter.

At shooting ducks I am a beaut.
There is no duck I cannot shoot,
In the eye, in the ear,
In the index finger.

In Frisco Bay there lives a whale
And she eats pork chops by the pail,
By the hatbox, by the pillbox,
By the hogshead and schooner.

Her name is Lena, she's a peach,
But don't leave food within her reach,
Or babies, or nursemaids,
Or chocolate ice cream sodas.

She loves to laugh, and when she smiles,
You just see teeth for miles and miles,
And tonsils, and spareribs
And things too fierce to mention.

She knows no games so when she plays,
She rolls her eyes for days and days,
She vibrates and yodels
And breaks the Ten Commandments.

Oh, what can you do in a case like that?
Oh, what can you do but stamp on your
        hat?
Or on an eggshell or a toothbrush
Or anything that's helpless!

Dunderbeck's Machine

There was a man from Pleasantville,
His name was Dunderbeck.
He sold a lot of sausages
And sauerkraut, by heck.
He made the greatest sausages
That you have ever seen
Until one day he invented
A sausage meat machine.

Chorus
Oh, Dunderbeck, oh, Dunderbeck,
How could you be so mean?
To ever have invented
Such a terrible machine?
Now alley cats and long-tailed rats
Will never more be seen.
They'll all be ground to sausage meat
In Dunderbeck's machine!

One day a little fat boy came
A-walking in the store.
He bought a pound of sausages
And laid them on the floor.
Then he began to whistle,
He whistled up a tune.
The sausages they jumped and barked
And danced around the room.

Chorus

One day the thing got busted.
The darn thing wouldn't work,
And Dunderbeck he crawled inside
To see what made it jerk.
His wife came walking in just then
Cause she walked in her sleep,
She gave the crank a heck of a yank,
And Dunderbeck was meat!

Chorus

So, if you have a cat or dog,
You better keep it locked.
'Cause if you don't. I'm warning you,
You're in for some big shock.
If ever you eat some sausage meat
From Dunderbeck right now,
You'll hear the little sausages
Meow and bow-wow-wow!

Chorus

20

Dunderbeck's Machine

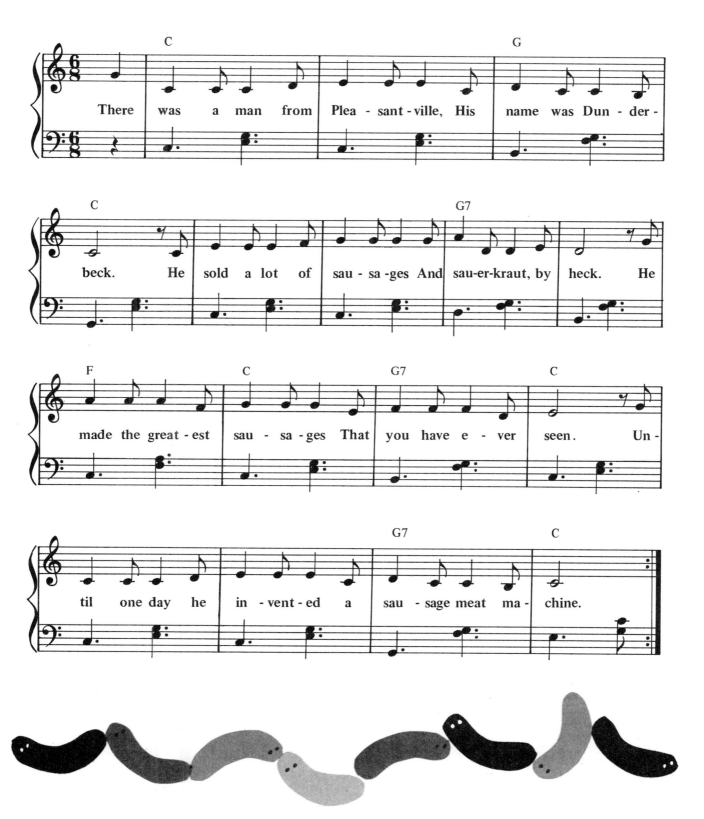

The Green Grass Grew All Around

The Green Grass Grew All Around

Now in a hole (now in a hole),
There was a tree (there was a tree),
The prettiest little tree (the prettiest little
    tree),
That you ever did see (that you ever did
    see).
The tree in a hole,
And the hole in the ground,
And the green grass grew all around, all
    around,
And the green grass grew all around.

Now on that tree (now on that tree),
There was a limb (there was a limb),
The prettiest little limb (the prettiest little
    limb)
That you ever did see (that you ever did
    see).
The limb on the tree,
And the tree in a hole,
And the hole in the ground,
And the green grass grew all around, all
    around,
And the green grass grew all around.

Now on this limb (now on this limb),
There was a branch (there was a branch),
The prettiest little branch (the prettiest
    little branch),
That you ever did see (that you ever did
    see.)
The branch on the limb,
And the limb on the tree,
And the tree in a hole,
And the hole in the ground,
And the green grass grew all around, all
    around,
And the green grass grew all around.

Now on this branch (now on this
    branch),
There was a bough (there was a bough),
The prettiest little bough (the prettiest
    little bough)
That you ever did see (that you ever did
    see).
The bough on the branch,
And the branch on the limb,
And the limb on the tree,
And the tree in a hole,
And the hole in the ground,
And the green grass grew all around,
    all around,
And the green grass grew all around.

Now on this bough (now on this bough),
There was a nest (there was a nest),
The prettiest little nest (the prettiest little
    nest)
That you ever did see (that you ever did
    see).
The nest on the bough,
And the bough on the branch,
And the branch on the limb,
And the limb on the tree,
And the tree in a hole,
And the hole in the ground,
And the green grass grew all around,
    all around,
And the green grass grew all around.

The Green Grass Grew All Around (continued)

Now on this nest (now on this nest),
There was a bird (there was a bird),
The prettiest little bird (the prettiest little
bird)
That you ever did see (that you ever did
see).
The bird on the nest,
And the nest on the bough,
And the bough on the branch,
And the branch on the limb,
And the limb on the tree,
And the tree in a hole,
And the hole in the ground,
And the green grass grew all around,
all around,
And the green grass grew all around.

Now in this bird (now in this bird)
There was a worm (there was a worm),
The prettiest little worm (the prettiest
little worm)
That you ever did see (that you ever did
see).
The worm in the bird,
And the bird on the nest,
And the nest on the bough,
And the bough on the branch,
And the branch on the limb,
And the limb on the tree,
And the tree in a hole,
And the hole in the ground,
And the green grass grew all around,
all around,
And the green grass grew all around.

Now on that worm (now on that worm),
There was a flea (there was a flea),
The prettiest little flea (the prettiest little
flea)
That you ever did see (that you ever did
see).
The flea on the worm,
And the worm in the bird,
And the bird on the nest,
And the nest on the bough,
And the bough on the branch,
And the branch on the limb,
And the limb on the tree,
And the tree in a hole,
And the hole in the ground,
And the green grass grew all around,
all around,
And the green grass grew all around.

Now on this flea (now on this flea),
There was a germ (there was a germ),
The prettiest little germ (the prettiest little
germ)
That you ever did see (that you ever did
see).
The germ on the flea,
And the flea on the worm,
And the worm in the bird,
And the bird on the nest,
And the nest on the bough,
And the bough on the branch,
And the branch on the limb,
And the limb on the tree,
And the tree in a hole,
And the hole in the ground,
And the green grass grew all around,
all around,
And the green grass grew all around.

The Green Grass Grew All Around *(continued)*

And now this germ (and now this germ),
Fell on the ground (fell on the ground),
The prettiest little ground, (the prettiest
    little ground),
That you ever did see (that you ever did
    see).
The ground on the germ,
And the germ on the flea,
And the flea on the worm,
And the worm in the bird,
And the bird on the nest,
And the nest on the bough,
And the bough on the branch,
And the branch on the limb,
And the limb on the tree,
And the tree in a hole,
And the hole in the ground,
And the green grass grew all around,
    all around,
And the green grass grew all around.

Now in the ground (now in the ground),
There was a hole (there was a hole),
The prettiest little hole (the prettiest little
    hole)
That you ever did see (that you ever did
    see).
The hole in the ground,
And the ground on the germ,
And the germ on the flea,
And the flea on the worm,
And the worm in the bird,
And the bird on the nest,
And the nest on the bough,
And the bough on the branch,
And the branch on the limb,
And the limb on the tree,
And the tree in a hole,
And the hole in the ground,
And the green grass grew all around,
    all around,
And the green grass grew all around.

Now in this hole (now in this hole)
There was a tree (there was a tree)
The prettiest little tree (the prettiest little
    tree)
That you ever did see (that you ever did
    see).
The tree in the hole
And the hole in the ground,
And the green grass grew all around,
    all around,
And the green grass grew all around.

And now you go back to verse #1 and start all over again! It is truly endless!

Popeye the Sailor Man

I'm Popeye, the sailor man.
I live in a caravan.
I open the door
And fall through the floor
I'm Popeye, the sailor man.

I'm Popeye, the sailor man.
I live in a garbage can.
It's cramped and it's crude,
But I get lots of food,
I'm Popeye, the sailor man.

I'm Popeye, the sailor man.
I live in a moving van.
I go where I'm sent
And I save on the rent,
I'm Popeye, the sailor man.

I'm Popeye, the sailor man.
I'm doing the best I can.
I eat all my spinach,
I fight to the finish,
I'm Popeye, the sailor man.

SHAKING IT UP

If You're Happy and You Know It

And you can show that you're happy in any other way you want, too. For example, if you're happy and you know it:

snap your fingers *(snap, snap)*
tap your toes *(tap, tap)*
blink your eyes *(blink, blink)*
nod your head *(nod, nod)*

shake your belly *(shake, shake)*
jump up high *(jump, jump)*
spin around *(spin, spin)*, etc.

If You're Happy and You Know It

If you're happy and you know it, clap
    your hands *(clap, clap)*.
If you're happy and you know it, clap
    your hands *(clap, clap)*.
If you're happy and you know it,
Then you really ought to show it,
If you're happy and you know it,
Clap your hands *(clap, clap)*.

If you're happy and you know it, stamp
    your feet *(stamp, stamp)*,
If you're happy and you know it, stamp
    your feet *(stamp, stamp)*,
If you're happy and you know it,
Then you really ought to show it,
If you're happy and you know it, stamp
    your feet *(stamp, stamp)*.

If you're happy and you know it, laugh
    out loud *(ha, ha!)*,
If you're happy and you know it, laugh
    out loud *(ha, ha!)*,
If you're happy and you know it,
Then you really ought to show it,
If you're happy and you know it, laugh
    out loud *(ha, ha!)*.

If you're happy and you know it, sing a
    song *(la, la)*,
If you're happy and you know it, sing a
    song *(la, la)*,
If you're happy and you know it,
Then you really ought to show it,
If you're happy and you know it, sing a
    song *(la, la)*.

If you're happy and you know it, shout
    hooray *(hoo-ray!)*,
If you're happy and you know it, shout
    hooray *(hoo-ray!)*,
If you're happy and you know it,
Then you really ought to show it,
If you're happy and you know it, shout
    hooray *(hoo-ray!)*.

One Finger, One Thumb

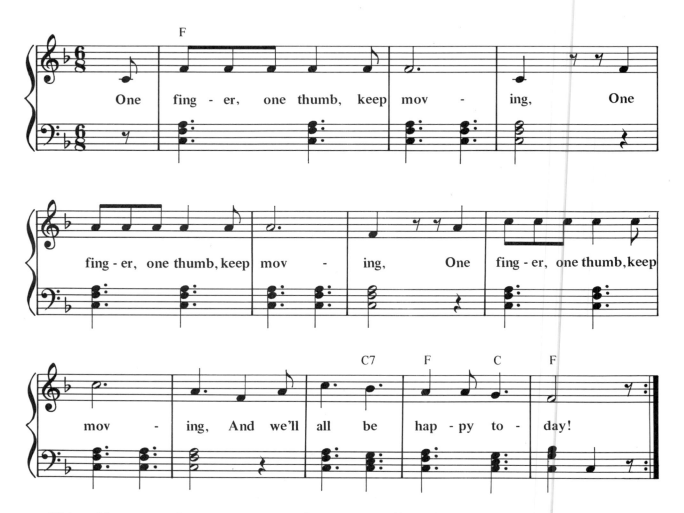

This add-on song becomes more and more complicated, and you really have to focus on it sharply to keep it going.

Start by moving one finger and one thumb of the same hand and move more body parts as the song directs. On the arm part, stretch each arm straight up to the ceiling. On the leg part, shake your leg. When you sing, "Keep moving," walk with your feet in place, whether you're standing or sitting. If you're standing to begin with, reverse the "stand up, sit down," to "sit down, stand up." If you want to add more, on the last line, "And we'll all be happy today," cross your arms in front of you down low, and then circle the arms across each other and into a high circle, bringing them back out to the side and ending up with them down alongside your body.

One Finger, One Thumb

One finger, one thumb, keep moving,
One finger, one thumb, keep moving,
One finger, one thumb, keep moving,
And we'll all be happy today.

One finger, one thumb, one hand, keep
   moving,
One finger, one thumb, one hand, keep
   moving,
One finger, one thumb, one hand, keep
   moving,
And we'll all be happy today.

One finger, one thumb, one hand, two
   hands, keep moving,
One finger, one thumb, one hand, two
   hands, keep moving,
One finger, one thumb, one hand, two
   hands, keep moving,
And we'll all be happy today.

One finger, one thumb, one hand, two
   hands, one arm, keep moving,
One finger, one thumb, one hand, two
   hands, one arm, keep moving,
One finger, one thumb, one hand, two
   hands, one arm, keep moving,
And we'll all be happy today.

One finger, one thumb, one hand, two
   hands, one arm, two arms, keep
   moving,
One finger, one thumb, one hand, two
   hands, one arm, two arms, keep
   moving,
One finger, one thumb, one hand, two
   hands, one arm, two arms, keep
   moving,
And we'll all be happy today.

One finger, one thumb, one hand, two
   hands, one arm, two arms, one
   leg, keep moving,
One finger, one thumb, one hand, two
   hands, one arm, two arms, one
   leg, keep moving,
One finger, one thumb, one hand, two
   hands, one arm, two arms, one
   leg, keep moving,
And we'll all be happy today.

One finger, one thumb, one hand, two
   hands, one arm, two arms, one
   leg, two legs, keep moving,
One finger, one thumb, one hand, two
   hands, one arm, two arms, one
   leg, two legs, keep moving,
One finger, one thumb, one hand, two
   hands, one arm, two arms, one
   leg, two legs, keep moving,
And we'll all be happy today.

One finger, one thumb, one hand, two
   hands, one arm, two arms, one
   leg, two legs, stand up, sit
   down, keep moving,
One finger, one thumb, one hand, two
   hands, one arm, two arms, one
   leg, two legs, stand up, sit
   down, keep moving,
One finger, one thumb, one hand, two
   hands, one arm, two arms, one
   leg, two legs, stand up, sit
   down, keep moving,
And we'll all be happy today.

Head, Shoulders, Baby

This syncopated song from the Georgia Islands is great fun to sing, especially when you clap on the rests between the "one-two" and the "two-three." If you want to make your life more complicated, clap in front of you on the first clap, in back of you on the second. You may also want to add a knee bend on each clap: that really makes the song bounce. You can also reverse the song, returning part by part back to "Chest, shoulders, baby," and finishing with "That's all, baby, one, two, three!"

Head, shoulders, baby, one *(clap)*, two *(clap)*, three.
Head, shoulders, baby, one *(clap)*, two *(clap)*, three.
Head, shoulders, head, shoulders,
Head, shoulders, baby, one *(clap)*, two *(clap)*, three.

Shoulders, chest, baby, one *(clap)*, two *(clap)*, three.
Shoulders, chest, baby, one *(clap)*, two *(clap)*, three.
Shoulders, chest, shoulders, chest,
Shoulders, chest, baby, one *(clap)*, two *(clap)*, three.

Chest, belly, baby, one *(clap)*, two *(clap)*, three.
Chest, belly, baby, one *(clap)*, two *(clap)*, three.
Chest, belly, chest, belly,
Chest, belly, baby, one *(clap)*, two *(clap)*, three.

Belly, knees, baby, one *(clap)*, two *(clap)*, three.
Belly, knees, baby, one *(clap)*, two *(clap)*, three.
Belly, knees, belly, knees,
Belly, knees, baby, one *(clap)*, two *(clap)*, three.

Knees, ankles, baby, one *(clap)*, two *(clap)*, three.
Knees, ankles, baby, one *(clap)*, two *(clap)*, three.
Knees, ankles, knees, ankles,
Knees, ankles, baby, one *(clap)*, two *(clap)*, three.

Head, Shoulders, Baby

Ev'rybody Loves Saturday Night

34

Ev'rybody Loves Saturday Night

This highly-charged one-line syncopated clapping song from Sierra Leone, West Africa, can be sung effectively in many languages.

Ev'rybody loves Saturday night.
Ev'rybody loves Saturday night,
(clap) Ev'rybody *(clap)*, ev'rybody,
(clap) Ev'rybody *(clap)*, ev'rybody,
(clap) Ev'rybody loves Saturday night!

For a change you may want to sing as the last line: *(clap)* All the cats dig Saturday night the most!

To sing this song in other languages, try:

French: Tout le monde aime Samedi soir!
Chinese: *(sounds like)* Ren ren si huan pai lu wansung!
Russian: *(sounds like)* Vussa lubyet pet vuh Subbotu vietcherom!
Yiddish: *(sounds like)* Yeder eyne hut lieb Shabas ba nacht!
Spanish: *(sounds like)* A todos les gusta la noche del Sadádo!
Nigerian: *(sounds like)* Kowa-yana son rana-Sati!
Czechoslovakian: *(sounds like)* Kashdee ma rad Sobotni vecher!

Wriggledy Jiggledy Song

Wriggledy jiggledy, here we go,
Crawling along with our heads down low.
Flat on our bellies, we wiggle along
Singing this wriggledy jiggledy song.

Wriggledy-jiggledy-jiggledy-jong,
We're having fun as we're crawling along.
We'll wiggle and wriggle and jiggle along
Until we have finished this wriggledy song!

JUMP ROPE
SONGS & CHANTS

Teddy Bear, Teddy Bear

This jump rope chant goes on and on. Each person that jumps in has a turn to jump each stanza and then jump out, as the next one jumps in. The music repeats as a chant, in an almost monotonous way, because all the energy must be used for jumping and doing the actions required by the words. For example, lift each knee as you "go upstairs," and "pray" with hands as you "say your prayers."

If you want to jump both stanzas, then change the last line of the first stanza to "I'm not through!" and continue with the second stanza.

Teddy bear, teddy bear, turn around.
Teddy bear, teddy bear, touch the
    ground.
Teddy bear, teddy bear, tie your shoe,
Teddy bear, teddy bear, please ski-doo!

Teddy bear, teddy bear, go upstairs,
Teddy bear, teddy bear, say your prayers,
Teddy bear, teddy bear, switch off the
    light,
Teddy bear, teddy bear, say (*spoken*)
    "good night."

Miss Polly Had a Dolly

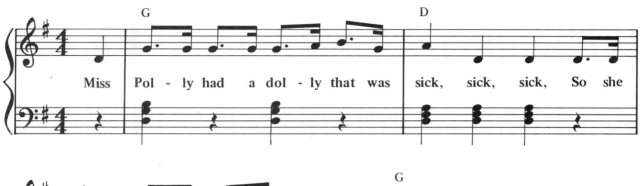

Miss Pol - ly had a dol - ly that was sick, sick, sick, So she

called for the doc - tor to come quick, quick, quick. The

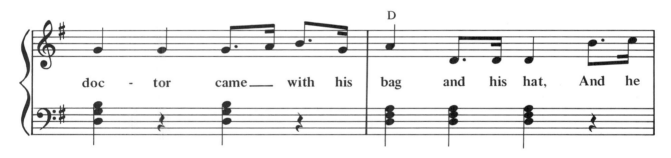

doc - tor came___ with his bag and his hat, And he

rapped on the door___ with a rat - tat - tat!

Miss Polly had a dolly that was sick,
    sick, sick,
So she called for the doctor to come
    quick, quick, quick.
The doctor came with his bag and his
    hat,
And he rapped on the door with a rat-tat-
    tat.

He looked at the dolly and he shook his
    head,
He said, "Miss Polly, put her straight to
    bed!"
He wrote on some paper for a pill, pill,
    pill,
"I'll be back in the morning with the bill,
    bill, bill!"

Miss Lucy Had a Baby

Miss Lucy had a baby,
She named him Tiny Tim.
She put him in the bathtub
To see if he could swim.

He drank up all the water,
He ate up all the soap,
He tried to eat the bathtub,
But it wouldn't go down his throat.

Miss Lucy called the Doctor,
Miss Lucy called the Nurse,
Miss Lucy called the lady
With the alligator purse.

"Measles," said the Doctor,
"Mumps," said the Nurse,
"A virus," said the lady
With the alligator purse.

"Penicillin," said the Doctor,
"Bed rest," said the Nurse,
"Pizza," said the lady
With the alligator purse.

"He'll live," said the Doctor,
"He's all right," said the Nurse,
"I'm leaving," said the lady
With the alligator purse.

JUMP ROPE CHANTS

Did You Eever, Ivver, Ever?

Did you eever, ivver, ever,
In your leaf, loaf, life,
See the deevel, divil, devil,
Kiss his weef, woaf, wife.
No I neever, niver, never
In my leaf, loaf, life,
Saw the deevel, divil, devil
Kiss his weef, woaf, wife.

Have you eever, ivver, ever
In your long-legged life
Seen a bowlegged sailor
With a knock-kneed wife?
No, I've neever, nivver, never
In my long-legged life
Seen a bowlegged sailor
With a knock-kneed wife!

My Father Is a Butcher

My father is a butcher,
My mother cuts the meat,
And I'm a little hot dog
That runs around the street.

Quiet, Please!

Order in the courtroom—
The monkey wants to speak!
No laughing—
No talking—
No showing your teeth!

Are You Coming Out, Sir?

Are you coming out, sir?
No, sir.
Why, sir?
Because I have a cold, sir.
Where'd you get your cold, sir?
At the North Pole, sir.
What were you doing there, sir?
Catching polar bears, sir.
How many did you catch, sir?
One, sir, two, sir, three, sir.
That's enough for me, sir!

MORE JUMP ROPE CHANTS

I Is Tired

I is tired,
I is weary,
Picks I up
And kiss I dearie.

"Is you cold?"
"Nearly fwoze."
"Want my coat?"
"Just the sleeves."
"Full or empty?"
"Full, please!"

Midnight on the Ocean

It was midnight on the ocean,
Not a taxi was in sight.
The sun was shining brightly
And it rained all day that night!

Little Miss Crimson

Little Miss Crimson dressed in blue
Died last night at half past two.
Before she died, she told me this,
"When I jump rope I always miss!"
  (jump fast until you miss)

Johnny Over the Ocean

Johnny over the ocean
Johnny over the sea.
Johnny broke a milk bottle
And blamed it all on me!

Numbers

Number one, touch your tongue.
Number two, touch your shoe.
Number three, touch your knee.
Number four, touch the floor.
Number five, touch your side.
Number six, pick up sticks.
Number seven, point to heaven.
Number eight, close the gate.
Number nine, touch your spine.
Number ten, do it over again!

I Went Downtown

I went downtown to see a clown.
He gave me a nickel to buy a pickle.
The pickle was sour; he gave me a
    flower.
The flower was dead; he gave me a
    thread.
The thread was black; he gave me a
    smack.
The smack was hard; he gave me a card.
The card was bright; he gave me a light.
The light exploded; we all got corroded!

ON THE ROAD!

The Wheels on the Bus

The Wheels on the Bus

The wheels on the bus go round and
round,
Round and round, round and round.
The wheels on the bus go round and
round,
All through the town.

The conductor on the bus says, "Tickets,
please!
Tickets, please, tickets, please!"
The conductor on the bus says, "Tickets,
please!"
All through the town.

The people on the bus go up and down,
Up and down, up and down.
The people on the bus go up and down,
All through the town.

The driver on the bus says, "Move to
the rear,
Move to the rear, move to the rear!"
The driver on the bus says, "Move to
the rear,"
All through the town.

The horn on the bus goes, "Beep, beep,
beep,
Beep, beep, beep, beep, beep, beep."
The horn on the bus goes, "Beep, beep,
beep,"
All through the town.

The wipers on the bus go, "Swish,
swish, swish,
Swish, swish, swish, swish, swish,
swish."
The wipers on the bus go "Swish, swish,
swish,"
All through the town.

The children on the bus go, "Chatter,
chatter, chatter,
Chatter, chatter, chatter, chatter, chatter,
chatter,"
The children on the bus go, "Chatter,
chatter, chatter,"
All through the town.

The babies on the bus go, "Waah, waah,
waah,
Waah, waah, waah, waah, waah, waah,"
The babies on the bus go, "Waah, waah,
waah,"
All through the town.

She'll Be Comin' Round the Mountain

She'll Be Comin' Round the Mountain

She'll be comin' round the mountain
    when she comes *(when she comes)*,
She'll be comin' round the mountain
    when she comes *(when she comes)*,
She'll be comin' round the mountain,
She'll be comin' round the mountain,
She'll be comin' round the mountain
    when she comes.

This marvelous song has as many verses as you can imagine. Try these and then make up your own!

She'll be driving six white horses when she comes.

She'll be shinin' just like silver when she comes.

And we'll all go out to meet her when she comes.

She'll be breathin' smoke and fire when she comes.

She will neither rock nor totter when she comes.

She will run so smooth and steady when she comes.

We'll be singin' "hallelujah" when she comes.

We will kill the old red rooster when she comes.

And we'll all have chicken and dumplings when she comes.

She will take us to the portals when she comes.

What Did Delaware, Boys?

Oh, what did Delaware, boys, oh, what did Delaware?
Oh, what did Delaware, boys, oh, what did Delaware?
Oh, what did Delaware, boys, oh, what did Delaware?
I ask you now as a personal friend, what did Delaware?

She wore her New Jersey, boys, she wore her New Jersey.
She wore her New Jersey, boys, she wore her New Jersey.
She wore her New Jersey, boys, she wore her New Jersey.
I tell you now as a personal friend, she wore her New Jersey.

And it goes on and on with verses for at least fourteen more states. Try these:

Florida: Oh, how did FLORI-DIE (*Flora die*), boys?
Missouri: She died in MISSOURI (*misery*), boys.
Iowa: Oh, what does IO-WA (*Io weigh*), boys?
Washington: She weighs a WASHING-TON, boys.
Idaho: Oh, what does IDA-HO (*Ida hoe*), boys?
Maryland: She hoes her MARY-LAND, boys.

Tennessee: Oh, what does TENNES-SEE, boys?
Arkansas: She sees what ARKAN-SAS (*Arkan saw*), boys.
Oregon: Oh, where has ORE-GON (*Ore-gone*), boys?
Oklahoma: She's gone to OKLA-HOMA (*Okla-hom-a*), boys.
Massachusetts: Oh, what did MASSA-CHEW, boys?
Connecticut: She chewed her CONNECTI-CUD, boys.

What Did Delaware, Boys?

Train Is A-Comin'

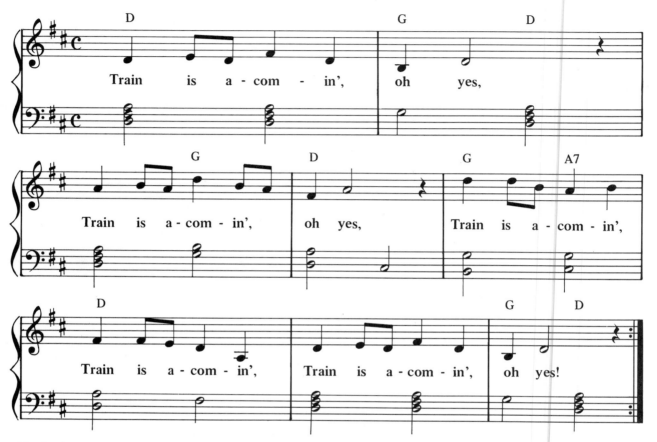

Train is a-comin', oh yes,
Train is a-comin', oh yes,
Train is a-comin',
Train is a-comin',
Train is a-comin', oh yes!

Better get your ticket, oh yes,
Better get your ticket, oh yes,
Better get your ticket,
Better get your ticket,
Better get your ticket, oh yes!

Going through a tunnel, oh yes,
Going through a tunnel, oh yes,
Going through a tunnel,
Going through a tunnel,
Going through a tunnel, oh yes!

And this song, too, will continue to as many verses as you please. Here are a few:

Coming out to daylight, oh yes!

Going very s-l-o-w-l-y, oh yes!

Stopping at the station, oh yes!

Going fast and faster, oh yes!

Collecting all the tickets, oh yes!

REAL MEAN

The Cat Came Back

Old Mis - ter John - son had trou - bles of his own. He had a yel - low cat and it would-n't leave home. He tried and he tried to give the cat a-way. He gave it to a man go - ing off to Bom- bay.

CHORUS:

But the cat came back, the ve - ry next day. The cat came back, thought it was a go -ner, but the cat came back 'cause it could - n't stay a - way.

The Cat Came Back

Old Mister Johnson had troubles of his
    own.
He had a yellow cat and it wouldn't
    leave home.
He tried and he tried to give the cat
    away.
He gave it to a man going off to
    Bombay.

Chorus

But the cat came back the very next day.
The cat came back, thought it was a
    goner,
But the cat came back 'cause it couldn't
    stay away.

He gave it to a man going way out west;
Told him to take it to the one he loved
    the best.
The train hit the curve, and then it
    jumped the rail.
Not a soul was left behind to tell the
    gruesome tale.

Chorus

Gave it to a gambler with a dollar note
Told him to take it up the river in a
    boat.
Tied a rope around its neck that must
    have weighed a pound.
Now they drag the river for the gambler
    that is drowned.

Chorus

Gave it to a feller up in a balloon.
Telling him to take it to the man in the
    moon.
The balloon it busted and everybody said
Ten miles away they picked up that feller
    good and dead.

Chorus

The farmer swore he'd kill the yellow cat
    on sight,
Loaded up his shotgun with nails and
    dynamite.
Waited and he waited for it to come
    around.
Ninety-seven pieces of the man is all
    they found.

Chorus

Way across the ocean they sent the cat
    at last,
Vessel only out a day and taking water
    fast.
People all began to pray, the boat began
    to toss.
Great big gust of wind came by and
    every soul was lost.

Chorus

(More about the cat on the next page.)

The Cat Came Back *(continued)*

On a telegraph wire, sparrows in a
    bunch.
Cat was feeling hungry, thought they'd be
    good for lunch.
Climbed softly up the pole, and when it
    reached the top,
Stepped on the 'lectric wire which tied it
    in a knot.

Chorus

The cat got discouraged and thought the
    thing to do,
Was to take a vacation upon the ocean
    blue.
So it took a voyage to six foreign cities.
And came home one month later with six
    little kitties.

Chorus

Cat was a possessor of a family of its
    own,
With six little kittens, till there came a
    cyclone.
Blew the house all apart and tossed the
    cat around.
The air was full of kittens; not one was
    ever found.

Chorus

Oh, John the Rabbit

Oh, John the rabbit,
Yes, Ma'am,
Got a rotten habit,
Yes, Ma'am,
Jumping in my garden,
Yes, Ma'am,
Eating all my cabbage,
Yes, Ma'am,
My sweet potatoes,
Yes, Ma'am,
My fresh tomatoes,
Yes, Ma'am,
And if I live,
Yes, Ma'am,
To see next fall,
Yes, Ma'am,
I ain't gonna have,
Yes, Ma'am,
No veggies at all,
Yes, Ma'am,

Oh, John the rabbit,
Yes, Ma'am,
Got a rotten habit,
Yes, Ma'am,
Jumping in my garden,
Yes, Ma'am,
Eating all my stringbeans,
Yes, Ma'am,
My white turnips,
Yes, Ma'am,
My sweet parsnips,
Yes, Ma'am,
And if I live,
Yes, Ma'am,
I ain't gonna have,
Yes, Ma'am,
No veggies at all,
Yes, Ma'am,

Oh, John the Rabbit

Whoever Shall Have Peanuts

Who - ev - er shall have some good pea - nuts, and giv - eth his neigh - bor none, Then he can't have a - ny of my good pea - nuts, when his good pea - nuts are done.

CHORUS:

Oh, won't it be joy - ful, joy - ful, joy - ful. Oh, won't it be joy - ful, when his good pea - nuts are gone!

Whoever Shall Have Peanuts

Whoever shall have some good peanuts,
And giveth his neighbor none,
Then he can't have any of my good
    peanuts,
When his good peanuts are done.

Chorus
Oh, won't it be joyful,
Joyful, joyful,
Oh, won't it be joyful,
When his good peanuts are gone!

Now you can take turns adding your own "fancier" verses. Don't stop with just peanuts. Here you can add as many words as you want, anywhere you want. For example, you could sing:

Whoever shall have some good, gooey,
    glitzy gumdrops,
And giveth his nosy, nasty, notorious
    neighbor none.
Then he can't have any of my good,
    gooey, glitzy gumdrops,
When his good, gooey, glitzy gumdrops
    are done.

Or you could sing:

"Whoever shall have some perky,
pip-snortin', palate-pleasing popcorn,"
           or
"Whoever shall have some jam-bam,
jiggledy, joshy, juicy jelly beans,"
           or
"Whoever shall have some 'I scream,
          You scream,
          We all scream,
          for Ice Cream,' "
and so on.

Turn the page to see how to fit the words into the music.

Whoever Shall Have Peanuts *(continued)*

Who-ev-er shall have some good, goo-ey, glit-zy gum drops and

giv-eth his nos-y, nas-ty, no-to-ri-ous neigh-bor none ___,

Then he can't have a-ny of my good, goo-ey, glit-zy

gum drops, when his good, goo-ey, glit-zy gum drops are gone.

Mama Don't 'Low

Mama don't 'low no banjo-playin' round
    here.
Mama don't 'low no banjo-playin' round
    here.
Well, I don't care what Mama don't 'low,
Gonna play my banjo anyhow.
Mama don't 'low no banjo-playin' round
    here.

(More about what
Mama don't 'low
on the next page.)

Mama Don't 'Low *(continued)*

Mama don't 'low no rock-song-singin'
    round here.
Mama don't 'low no rock-song-singin'
    round here.
Well, I don't care what Mama don't 'low,
Gonna sing my head off anyhow.
Mama don't 'low no rock-song-singin'
    round here.

Mama don't 'low no stupid talk round
    here.
Mama don't 'low no stupid talk round
    here.
Well, I don't care what Mama don't 'low,
Gonna shoot my mouth off anyhow.
Mama don't 'low no stupid talk round
    here.

Mama don't 'low no guitar-playin' round
    here.
Mama don't 'low no guitar-playin' round
    here.
Well, I don't care what Mama don't 'low,
Gonna play my guitar anyhow.
Mama don't 'low no guitar playin' round
    here.

GET
THE
MESSAGE

Run Along Home

Now run a-long home and jump in the tub.

Soap your-self and rub-a-dub-dub. The

ver-y same thing I say un-to you,

"Wash in the Spring and Sat-ur-day, too."

Now run along home
And jump in the tub,
Soap yourself
And rub-a-dub-dub.

The very same thing
I say unto you,
"Wash in the Spring
And Saturday, too."

Now run along home
And clean up your room.
Straighten up
And sweep with a broom.

The very same thing,
I say unto you,
"Let's keep it clean
Until we get through."

Now run along home
And do your homework
Finish it so
You aren't a jerk.

The very same thing
I say unto you,
"I'll do my work,
If you do it too!"

Run Along Home

Now run along home
And jump into bed.
Say your prayers
And cover your head.

The very same thing
I say unto you.
"You dream of me,
And I'll dream of you!"

You Can't Make a Turtle Come Out

By Malvina Reynolds

You can't make a tur - tle come out, You can't make a tur - tle come out. You can call him or coax him Or shake him or shout, But you can't make a tur - tle come out, come out, You can't make a tur - tle come out ____ .

You Can't Make a Turtle Come Out (continued)

You can't make a turtle come out,
You can't make a turtle come out.
You can call him or coax him
Or shake him or shout,
But you can't make a turtle come out,
    come out,
You can't make a turtle come out.

If he wants to stay in his shell,
If he wants to stay in his shell,
You can knock on the door, but
You can't ring the bell,
And you can't make a turtle come out,
    come out.
You can't make a turtle come out.

Be kind to your four-footed friends,
Be kind to your four-footed friends.
A poke makes a turtle
Retreat at both ends,
And you can't make a turtle come out,
    come out,
You can't make a turtle come out.

So you'll have to patiently wait,
So you'll have to patiently wait,
And when he gets ready
He'll open the gate,
But you can't make a turtle come out,
    come out.
You can't make a turtle come out.

And when you forget that he's there,
And when you forget that he's there,
He'll be walking around
With his head in the air,
But you can't make a turtle come out,
    come out,
You can't make a turtle come out!

It Isn't Any Trouble Just to Smile

It isn't any trouble just to S-M-I-L-E.
It isn't any trouble just to S-M-I-L-E.
So smile when you're in trouble,
It will vanish like a bubble,
If you only take the trouble just to
    S-M-I-L-E!

It isn't any trouble just to L-A-U-G-H.
It isn't any trouble just to L-A-U-G-H.
So laugh when you're in trouble,
It will vanish like a bubble,
If you only take the trouble just to
    L-A-U-G-H.

It isn't any trouble just to ha-ha-ha-ha-ha!
It isn't any trouble just to ha-ha-ha-ha-ha!

So "ha!" when you're in trouble,
It will vanish like a bubble,
If you only take the trouble just to
HA-HA-HA-HA-HA!

It Isn't Any Trouble Just to Smile

Bye 'N' Bye

This song has a magical quality. It is incredibly simple and yet it creates its own mystery. I sang it to my children when they were little, and to the many thousands of children I have been singing with over the years. We lift our heads and point to each star separately in different parts of the sky. We decide before we start how many stars we will count, so we'd all be able to end the song together.

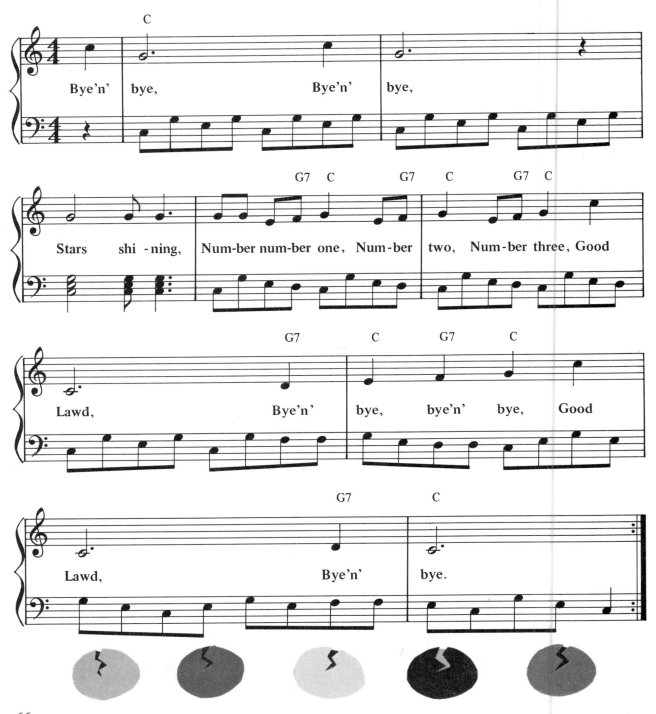

Bye 'N' Bye

Bye 'n' bye,
Bye 'n' bye,
Stars shining (shinin')
Number number one
Number two,
Number three (etc.)
Good Lawd,
Bye 'n' bye, bye 'n' bye,
Good Lawd,
Bye 'n' bye.

You can count other things, too, in this song besides stars. Instead of "Stars shining" you can sing:

> "flowers growing," (count flowers in the field)
> "rocks resting,"
> "birds flying,"
> "waves rippling," and anything else.

It Pays to Advertise!

The fish, it never cackles
'Bout its million eggs (or so),
The hen is quite a diff'rent bird,
One egg, and hear her crow!
The fish we spurn, but crown the hen,

Which leads me to surmise:
Don't hide your light, but blow your
    horn,
It pays to advertise!

(Music on next page.)

67

It Pays to Advertise! *(continued)*

The fish, it ne - ver ca - ckles 'bout its ___ mil - lion eggs (or so), The hen is quite a diff - 'rent bird, One ___ egg, and hear her crow! The fish we spurn, but crown the hen, Which leads me to sur - mise: Don't hide your light, but blow your horn, It ___ pays to ad - ver - tise!

REALLY
RIDICULOUS

Down by the Bay

Down by the bay (down by the bay),
Where the watermelons grow (where the
    watermelons grow),
Back to my home (back to my home),
I dare not go (I dare not go),
For if I do (for if I do),
My mother will say (my mother will say),
"Did you ever see a goose, kissing a
    moose?"
Down by the bay.

Down by the bay (down by the bay),
Where the watermelons grow (where the
    watermelons grow),
Back to my home (back to my home),
I dare not go (I dare not go),
For if I do (for if I do),
My mother will say (my mother will say),
"Did you ever see a mouse, cleaning her
    house?"
Down by the bay.

Mother can say just about anything. Here are just a few more possibilities:

"Did you ever see a seal, chewing his meal?"
Down by the bay.

"Did you ever see a baboon by the light
    of the moon?"
Down by the bay.

"Did you ever see a fly wearing a tie?"
Down by the bay.

"Did you ever see a cat getting too fat?"
Down by the bay.

"Did you ever see a bird being absurd?"
Down by the bay.

"You look like a bear when you don't
    comb your hair!"
Down by the bay.

"Did you ever see a calf play with a
    giraffe?"
Down by the bay.

Did you ever see a monkey, hugging a
    donkey?"
Down by the bay.

"Did you ever see a whale, with a polka-
    dot tail?"
Down by the bay.

Make up your own!

70

Down by the Bay

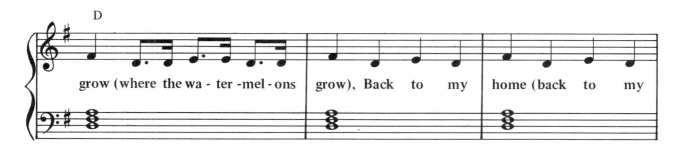

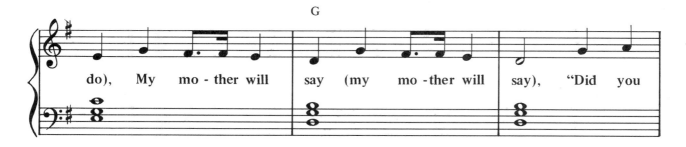

The Tailor and the Mouse

The Tailor and the Mouse

There was a tailor had a mouse,
Hi-diddle unkum feedle.
They lived together in one house,
Hi-diddle unkum feedle.

Chorus
Hi-diddle unkum ta-rum tan-tum,
Through the town of Ramsey,
Hi-diddle unkum, over the lea,
Hi-diddle unkum feedle.

The tailor had a tall silk hat,
Hi-diddle unkum feedle.
The mouse he ate it, fancy that!
Hi-diddle unkum feedle.

Chorus

The tailor thought the mouse was ill,
Hi-diddle unkum feedle.
He gave him part of a big blue pill,
Hi-diddle unkum feedle.

Chorus

The tailor thought the mouse would die,
Hi-diddle unkum feedle.
So he baked him up an apple pie,
Hi-diddle unkum feedle.

Chorus

The mouse ate it up and got all better,
Hi-diddle unkum feedle.
Sent the tailor a thank-you letter,
Hi-diddle unkum feedle.

Another version of this English folk song is not so up-beat:

The tailor thought the mouse would die,
Hi-diddle unkum feedle.
So he baked him in an apple pie,
Hi-diddle unkum feedle.

Chorus

The pie was cut, the mouse ran out,
Hi-diddle unkum feedle.
The tailor followed him about,
Hi-diddle unkum feedle.

Chorus

The tailor found his mouse was dead,
Hi-diddle unkum feedle.
So he caught another in his stead,
Hi-diddle unkum feedle.

Chorus

A Rooster Came Into Our Yard

A Rooster Came Into Our Yard

I had a hen, no eggs she gave,
I had a hen, no eggs she gave.
My wife said, "Honey, it isn't funny
To have a hen who gives no eggs."
One day a rooster came into our yard
And caught our hen right off her guard.
We're having eggs now, just like we
    used-ta,
Ever since the rooster came into our
    yard.

I had a dog, no pups she'd bear,
I had a dog, no pups she'd bear,
My wife said, "Honey, it isn't funny
To have a dog who bears no pups."
One day a rooster came into our yard
And caught our dog right off her guard.
We're having pooched eggs, just like we
    used-ta,
Ever since the rooster came into our
    yard.

I had a wife, no kids she'd bear
I had a wife, no kids she'd bear.
So I said, "Honey, it isn't funny
To have a wife who bears no kids."
One day a rooster came into our yard
And caught my wife right off her guard.
We're having egg-heads, just like we
    used-ta,
Ever since the rooster came into our
    yard.

I had a gum machine that gave no gum,
I had a gum machine that gave no gum.
My wife said, "Honey, it isn't funny
To have a gum machine that gives no
    gum."
One day a rooster came into our yard
And caught the gum machine right off its
    guard.
We're having chicklets, just like we used-
    ta,
Ever since the rooster came into our
    yard.

When Poppa Put the Paper on the Wall

When Pop-pa put the pa-per on the wall _____, He put a pile of pa-per in the hall _____. He pa-pered up the chairs. He pa-pered down the stairs. He e-ven put some pa-per on the wall. The lad-der tipped and he be-gan to fall _____. The paste fell down and

When Poppa Put the Paper on the Wall

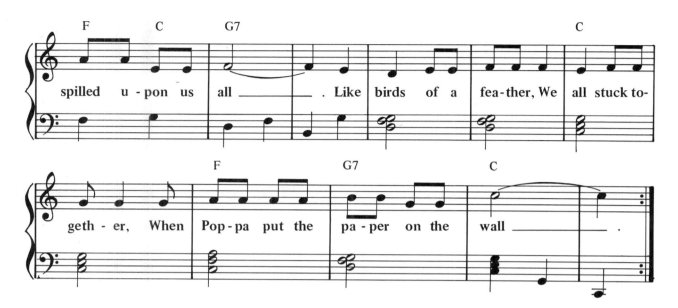

spilled u-pon us all ____ . Like birds of a fea-ther, We all stuck to-geth-er, When Pop-pa put the pa-per on the wall ____ .

When Poppa put the paper on the wall,
He put a pile of paper in the hall.
He papered up the chairs.
He papered down the stairs.
He even put some paper on the wall.
The ladder tipped and he began to fall.

The paste fell down and spilled upon us all.
Like birds of a feather,
We all stuck together,
When Poppa put the paper on the wall.

Itchy Flea

(spoken:) Flea flea—
         Flea fly—Flea fly—
         Flea fly mosquito, flea fly
         mosquito!
Oh, no no no more mosquitoes,
Oh, no no no more mosquitoes,
Itchy itchy, scratchy scratchy,
Oh, I got one down my backy—
Itchy itchy, scratchy scratchy,
Oh, I got one down my backy!
Beat that big bad bug with the bug
         spray—
Beat that big bad bug with the bug
         spray—
(spoken:) Shhh!

(Music on next page.)

Itchy Flea (continued)

78

LAST LAUGHS

Bile Them Cabbage Down

Once there was a little gal,
She came from way down south.
She had her hair done up so tight
She could hardly shut her mouth.

Chorus
Bile them cabbage down.
Spread the hoe-cake round.
The only song I ever sang
Was "Bile them cabbage down."

Her head was like a teapot,
Her nose was like the spout.
Her mouth was like the fireplace,
With the ashes all raked out.

Chorus

Took my gal to the blacksmith shop
To have her mouth made small.
She opened up that big ol' thing
And swallowed shop and all.

Chorus

Possum in a 'simmon tree,
Raccoon on the ground.
Raccoon says, "You son of a gun,
Shake some 'simmons down!"

Chorus

Someone stole my old coon dog,
Wish they'd bring him back.
He chased the big hogs through the fence
And the little ones through the crack.

Met a possum in the road,
Blind as he could be.
He jumped the fence and whipped my
        dog,
And bristled up at me.

Chorus

Once I had an old gray mule,
His name was Simon Slick.
He'd roll his eyes and back his ears,
And how that mule could kick!

Chorus

How that mule would fuss and fight,
Until his dying breath!
He shoved his hind feet down his throat
And kicked himself to death.

Chorus

Heard some folks tell stories that
There's gold in them thar hills.
But I've lived here for forty years,
And all I get is bills.

Bile Them Cabbage Down

Once there was a lit-tle gal, She came from way down south. She

had her hair done up so tight, She could hard-ly shut her mouth.

CHORUS:

Bile them cab-bage down. Spread the hoe-cake round. The

on-ly song I ev-er sang was "Bile them cab-bage down."

Mrs. Murphy's Chowder

The chorus of this crazy song is a real tongue twister. Sing it twice, if you dare.

Mrs. Murphy's Chowder (continued)

Won't you bring back, won't you bring
 back
Mrs. Murphy's chowder?
It was tuneful, every spoonful
Made you yodel louder.
After dinner Uncle Ben
Used to fill his fountain pen
From a plate of Mrs. Murphy's chowder.

Chorus

It had ice cream, cold cream, benzine,
 gasoline,
Soup greens, string beans, floating all
 around,
Sponge cake, beef steak, mistake,
 stomach ache,
Cream puffs, ear muffs, many to be
 found.
Silk hats, door mats, bed slats,
 democrats,
Door bells, church bells, beckon you to
 dine,
Meat balls, fish balls, moth balls, cannon
 balls,
Come on in, the chowder's fine!

Won't you bring back, won't you bring
 back,
Mrs. Murphy's chowder?
With each helping, you'll be yelping
For a headache powder.
And if they have it where we are,
You might find a red sports car,
In a plate of Mrs. Murphy's chowder.

Chorus

Won't you bring back, won't you bring
 back,
Mrs. Murphy's chowder?
You can pack it, you can stack it,
All around the larder.
The plumber died the other day
They embalmed him right away
In a bowl of Mrs. Murphy's chowder.

Chorus

Rabbit Ain't Got No Tail at All

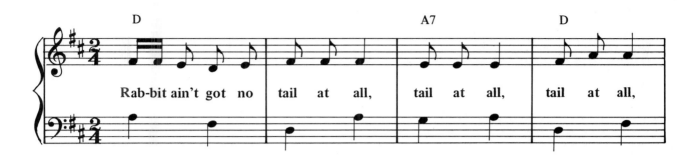

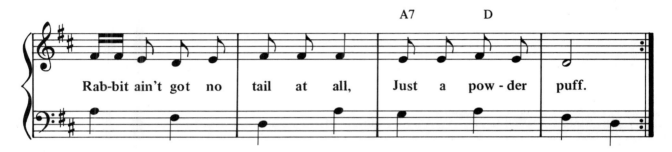

Rabbit ain't got no tail at all,
Tail at all, tail at all,
Rabbit ain't got no tail at all,
Just a powder puff!

Rabbit ain't got no fancy clothes,
Fancy clothes, fancy clothes,
Rabbit ain't got no fancy clothes,
Just his own fur coat!

Rabbit ain't got no limousine,
Limousine, limousine,
Rabbit ain't got no limousine,
Just his own fast feet!

Rabbit ain't got no pretty house,
Pretty house, pretty house,
Rabbit ain't got no pretty house,
Just a dark deep hole!

I've Got a Cold in My Nose—Kerchoo!

86

I've Got a Cold in My Nose—Kerchoo!

I've Got a Cold in My Nose—Kerchoo! *(continued)*

I feel blue,
I feel numb.
Oh, how I wish that spring would come.
I've got a cold in my nose—kerchoo!
I've got a cold in my nose—kerchoo!

I bought myself galoshes.
And a flannel union suit.
And on top of my galoshes
I put a pair of rubber boots.

Oh, I feel blue,
I feel numb.
Oh, how I wish that spring would come.
I've got a cold in my nose—kerchoo!
I've got a cold in my nose—kerchoo!

I went to the doctor
To see what he could do.
"Kerchoo," went the doctor,
"I think I've got one, too!"

So we both lay down
Side by side.
I'm still living,
But the poor doctor died.
I've got a cold in my nose—kerchoo!
I've got a cold in my nose—kerchoo!

When You Come to the End of a Lollipop

When you come to the end of a lollipop,
And you're left with just one more lick,
When you come to the end of a lollipop,
And you find that there's only the stick,
When you come to the end of a lollipop,
Then you STOP!

When You Come to the End of a Lollipop

Than I'll Ever Have With You!

I'll take the leg from some old ta-ble, I'll take the arm from some old chair, I'll take the neck from some old bot-tle, And from the horse I'll take the hair (I'll take the hair), And then I'll put them all to-geth-er, With the aid of string and glue, And I'll have more fun with the gosh darn dum-my than I'll ev-er have with you!

Than I'll Ever Have With You!

I'll take the leg from some old table,
I'll take the arm from some old chair,
I'll take the neck from some old bottle,
And from the horse I'll take the hair (I'll
    take the hair),

And then I'll put them all together,
With the aid of string and glue,
And I'll have more fun with the gosh
    darn dummy
Than I'll ever have with you!

91

Now You May Think

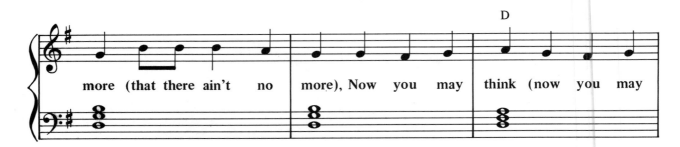

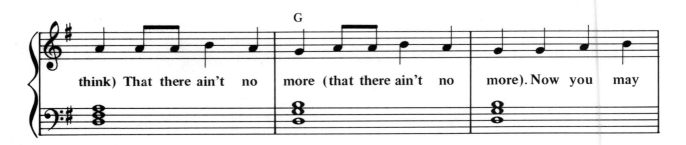

Now you may think (now you may think)
That there ain't no more (that there ain't
    no more),
Now you may think (now you may
    think),

That there ain't no more (that there ain't
    no more),
Now you may think that there ain't no
    more,
Well, there ain't!

INDEX

INDEX OF FIRST LINES

GUITAR CHORDS

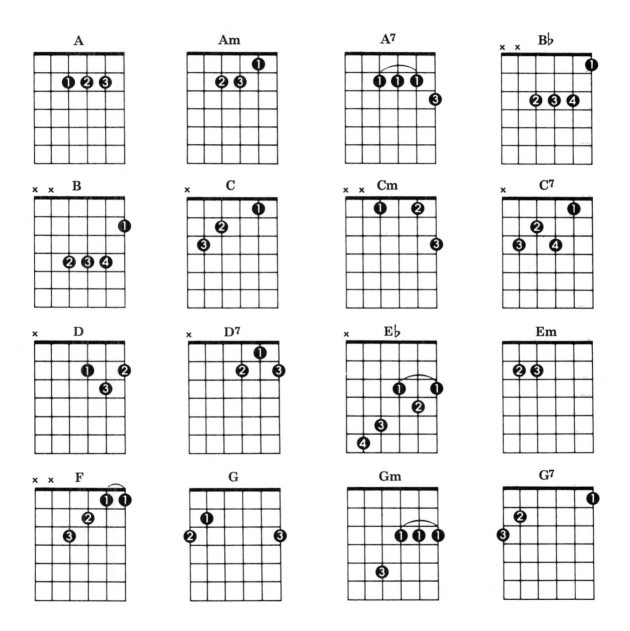

About the Author:
Esther L. Nelson, M.A., Dance Education, is one of the foremost educators in music and dance for children. She is the originator, with composer Bruce Haack, of the highly acclaimed "Dance, Sing and Listen" records and other music and dance participation recordings produced by her record company, Dimension 5. These records, the books she has written about music and movement and her much loved songbooks have already become classics and are used in schools, libraries and homes throughout the English-speaking world. Listed in *Who's Who of American Women* as well as *The World Who's Who of Women*, she conducts classes and workshops at colleges and educational conferences throughout the world to help teachers use movement and music to enhance the learning process.